YOU AND STRESS

A SURVIVAL GUIDE FOR ADOLESCENCE

By Gail C. Roberts, B.Ed., M.A.
and Lorraine Guttormson, M.A.

Edited by Rosemary Wallner

Free Spirit

PUBLISHING

10 9 8 7 6 5 4 3

Printed in the United States of America

Cover and book design by MacLean & Tuminelly

Supervising editor: Pamela Espeland

Free Spirit Publishing Inc.
400 First Avenue North, Suite 616
Minneapolis, MN 55401
(612) 338-2068

CONTENTS

CONTENTS

INTRODUCTION

You and Stress: A Survival Guide for Adolescence has been designed for you, with respect for your uniqueness and your potential. Working through it won't always be easy. The activities call upon you to be honest with yourself, to be open to new ideas, and to be willing to grow.

We hope the activities will lead you to some exciting discoveries about yourself and the world around you. We hope they will help you to understand and accept yourself, and to become more understanding and accepting of others. We hope they will give you a sense of having some degree of control over your life, and ultimately free you to be the best person you can be.

Gail C. Roberts, B.Ed., M.A.
Lorraine Guttormson, M.A.
August 1990

EUSTRESS AND DISTRESS

You are unique. Because you are unique, the things that stress you are different from the things that stress other people. You experience stress in your own way, and you handle it in your own way.

For example, you may become mildly annoyed by a particular *stressor* (source of stress). Another person may become very annoyed or upset by it. Still another person might become severely depressed or even suicidal in response to that same stressor.

Many people think that all stress is bad for you. In fact, there are two types of stress — and one is good for you.

• *Eustress* is stress caused by *happy* circumstances. Cheering for your team, winning a prize, getting a gift, meeting a new friend, or waiting for a happy event to start are all situations that cause eustress. Most people do not need help to deal with this type of stress.

• *Distress* is stress caused by *unhappy* circumstances. Being injured in an accident, failing in some way, being rejected, or losing someone you care about are all situations that cause distress. One person may feel distress about time, money, or health. Another person may feel distress about self-image, relationships, or the future. Many people need help dealing with this type of stress.

ACTIVITY 1

What are some sources of distress in your life? Read this list of possibilities. For each, put a check mark in the box that best describes how it affects you.

	never	sometimes	frequently	always
1. I am concerned about my eating habits.	☐	☐	☐	☐
2. I am concerned about my sleeping habits.	☐	☐	☐	☐
3. I am concerned about my personal hygiene (cleanliness).	☐	☐	☐	☐
4. I am concerned about my living conditions.	☐	☐	☐	☐
5. I am concerned about my physical health.	☐	☐	☐	☐
6. I am concerned about the physical health of people I know.	☐	☐	☐	☐
7. I am concerned about my mental health.	☐	☐	☐	☐
8. I am concerned about the mental health of people I know.	☐	☐	☐	☐
9. I am concerned about my grades in school.	☐	☐	☐	☐
10. I am concerned about how my peers treat me.	☐	☐	☐	☐
11. I am concerned about a teacher.	☐	☐	☐	☐
12. I am concerned about being late or disorganized.	☐	☐	☐	☐
13. I am concerned about meeting a parent's expectations.	☐	☐	☐	☐
14. I am concerned about not being loved.	☐	☐	☐	☐
15. I am concerned about having no one to talk to.	☐	☐	☐	☐
16. I am concerned about a problem with my parents.	☐	☐	☐	☐
17. I am concerned about the relationship between my parents.	☐	☐	☐	☐

	never	sometimes	frequently	always
18. I am concerned about being in a serious accident.	☐	☐	☐	☐
19. I am concerned about dying.	☐	☐	☐	☐
20. I am concerned about someone in my family dying.	☐	☐	☐	☐
21. I am concerned about being hurt emotionally.	☐	☐	☐	☐
22. I am concerned about being hurt physically.	☐	☐	☐	☐
23. I am concerned about being hurt sexually.	☐	☐	☐	☐
24. I am concerned about things I am ashamed of and have kept secret.	☐	☐	☐	☐
25. I am concerned about getting a good education.	☐	☐	☐	☐
26. I am concerned about my living arrangements.	☐	☐	☐	☐
27. I am concerned about my relationship with a female friend.	☐	☐	☐	☐
28. I am concerned about my relationship with a male friend.	☐	☐	☐	☐
29. I am concerned about getting someone pregnant or getting pregnant myself.	☐	☐	☐	☐
30. I am concerned about feelings I find hard to control.	☐	☐	☐	☐
31. I am concerned about actions I find hard to control.	☐	☐	☐	☐
32. I am concerned about being independent.	☐	☐	☐	☐
33. I am concerned about being rejected.	☐	☐	☐	☐
34. I am concerned about being shy.	☐	☐	☐	☐

	never	sometimes	frequently	always
35. I am concerned about my physical appearance.	☐	☐	☐	☐
36. I am concerned about what other people think of me.	☐	☐	☐	☐
37. I am concerned about not being trusted.	☐	☐	☐	☐
38. I am concerned about the amount of influence I have or don't have over people.	☐	☐	☐	☐
39. I am concerned about the amount of freedom I have.	☐	☐	☐	☐
40. I am concerned about my faults.	☐	☐	☐	☐
41. I am concerned that I am a failure.	☐	☐	☐	☐
42. I am concerned about money.	☐	☐	☐	☐
43. I am concerned about things I would like to have.	☐	☐	☐	☐
44. I am concerned about gambling.	☐	☐	☐	☐
45. I am concerned about drugs.	☐	☐	☐	☐
46. I am concerned about alcohol.	☐	☐	☐	☐
47. I am concerned about my friend's habits or problems.	☐	☐	☐	☐
48. I am concerned about being loved.	☐	☐	☐	☐
49. I am concerned about my future.	☐	☐	☐	☐
50. I am concerned about nuclear war.	☐	☐	☐	☐

	never	sometimes	frequently	always
51. I am concerned about religion.	☐	☐	☐	☐
52. I am concerned about…				

_____

_____

_____

_____   ☐   ☐   ☐   ☐

Something to think about

Distress can have a good side, too. It's a great motivator for activity that may get positive results — and it can be a force for positive personal change.

ACTIVITY 2

DOODLE CLUES

Some people think that doodles may contain clues to what's bothering you. Take a look at any doodles you've drawn on your school notebook. Can you remember who or what was on your mind when you drew them? What do you think your doodles tell you?

Use this space to doodle whatever you choose. Then study your doodles to see if you can find any clues to the sources of eustress or distress in your life.

THE FACE OF YOUR FEAR

What is your most distressing stressor? Use this space to draw a picture or write a poem about it.

*"Not everything that is faced can be changed.
But nothing can be changed until it is faced."*
James Baldwin

ACTIVITY 4

HOW DO OTHER PEOPLE HANDLE DISTRESS?

Different people handle distress in different ways. Think about, then write about how people you know usually handle their distress.

1. Your best friend:

_____

_____

_____

2. Your parent or guardian:

_____

_____

_____

3. Your brother or sister:

_____

_____

_____

4. Another person in your life who's important to you:

_____

_____

_____

5. How do *you* handle distress most of the time?

_____

_____

_____

How would you *like* to handle distress?

_____

_____

_____

FIGHT, FLIGHT, OR FREEZE: THREE REACTIONS TO STRESS

Psychologists have studied a variety of people in stressful situations. They have identified three common reactions to stress: fight, flight, or freeze.

• If you have a *fight reaction* to a stressor, you face your stressor and deal directly with it. For example, if you are surprised by a physical attack, you might defend yourself by fighting back.

• If you have a *flight reaction* to a stressor, you try to escape it — to get away from it in whatever way you can. For example, if you are caught in a raging fire, you will try to find a way out as fast as possible. If your stressor is a final exam, you might put off studying for it.

• If you have a *freeze reaction* to a stressor, you are immobilized by it, physically and mentally. Your body and brain try to block it out. For example, if your stressor is a grizzly bear, you might suddenly stop in your tracks and stay motionless.

You might have a different reaction to each stressor you encounter.

Think of a time when you had a fight reaction or saw someone else have a fight reaction. Describe what happened.

_____

_____

_____

Was this the *best* way to respond to the situation? YES ☐ NO ☐

Why or why not?

_____

_____

_____

Think of a time when you had a flight reaction or saw someone else have a flight reaction. Describe what happened.

_____

_____

_____

Was this the *best* way to respond to the situation? YES ☐ NO ☐

Why or why not?

_____

_____

_____

ACTIVITY 5

Think of a time when you had a freeze reaction or saw someone else have a freeze reaction. Describe what happened.

_____

_____

_____

Was this the *best* way to respond to the situation? YES ☐ NO ☐

Why or why not?

_____

_____

_____

IS DISTRESS MAKING YOU SICK?

When you are faced with a stressful situation, does your heart beat faster? Does your mouth get dry? Do your palms start to sweat? Does your face turn pale? These are some of the ways your body may respond to stress.

Physiology is the study of bodily functions and systems. Physiologists who study stress have learned these things about the way it affects the body:

• Seconds after your brain recognizes that you are under stress, your body releases adrenaline, which speeds up your body's systems.

• When you are under stress, your muscles need more glucose, a source of energy. Extra glucose is released by your liver and carried to your muscles.

• Because your muscles need more oxygen to turn the extra glucose into energy, your heart starts to pump harder. Your blood pressure rises, and your breathing becomes faster and deeper.

• Meanwhile, other systems slow down so more blood can go to your muscles. Digestion decreases as your salivary glands dry up and your stomach and intestines slow down or stop. You may turn pale as blood is diverted from blood vessels near the skin.

• Since your body is likely to overheat during times of stress, your skin cools itself by perspiring.

Usually these physiological responses last just long enough for you to react effectively and do something about the source of your distress. But if you take a long time to deal with a stressor, or if it occurs frequently, or never goes away, your body stays in a charged or semi-charged condition. After a time, this can literally make you sick! Exactly how depends on what kind of distress you are experiencing, where you feel it most, and where your body is weakest.

ACTIVITY 6

How does distress affect your health? Read this list of possibilities. For each, put a check mark in the box that best describes how it affects you.

	never	sometimes	frequently	always
1. I have headaches.	☐	☐	☐	☐
2. I have digestive problems (stomach aches, vomiting, constipation, diarrhea).	☐	☐	☐	☐
3. I have blurred vision.				
4. I have respiratory problems (shortness of breath, hyperventilation, asthma).	☐	☐	☐	☐
5. I have skin problems (acne, rashes, hives, eczema).	☐	☐	☐	☐
6. I have neck or back pain.	☐	☐	☐	☐
7. I feel a need to urinate.	☐	☐	☐	☐
8. I have muscle cramps.	☐	☐	☐	☐
9. I grind my teeth (while awake or asleep) or have tooth decay.	☐	☐	☐	☐
10. I have heartbeat irregularities (pounding, skipping a beat).	☐	☐	☐	☐
11. I have fainting spells (dizziness, nausea).	☐	☐	☐	☐
12. I have cold sweats and hot flashes.	☐	☐	☐	☐
13. I have allergies.	☐	☐	☐	☐
14. I have nervous twitches.	☐	☐	☐	☐
15. I have nervous habits (nail biting, smoking, gum chewing, hair twirling, fidgeting, tapping).	☐	☐	☐	☐
16. (If you are female): I have premenstrual tension.	☐	☐	☐	☐
17. I have sleep disorders (insomnia, oversleeping, nightmares).	☐	☐	☐	☐
18. I eat too much or too little.	☐	☐	☐	☐
19. I have eating disorders (bulimia or anorexia nervosa).	☐	☐	☐	☐

	never	sometimes	frequently	always
20. I use drugs (including alcohol).	☐	☐	☐	☐
21. I have flashbacks or memory lapses.	☐	☐	☐	☐
22. I laugh nervously or blush.	☐	☐	☐	☐
23. I feel like crying.	☐	☐	☐	☐
24. I feel depressed.	☐	☐	☐	☐
25. I feel panicky.	☐	☐	☐	☐
26. I feel hostile.	☐	☐	☐	☐
27. I feel jumpy.	☐	☐	☐	☐
28. I feel unable to concentrate.	☐	☐	☐	☐
29. I feel emotionally drained or physically exhausted.	☐	☐	☐	☐
30. I feel frustrated.	☐	☐	☐	☐
31. I feel irritable.	☐	☐	☐	☐
32. I feel overwhelmed.	☐	☐	☐	☐

33. I have other physical or mental problems that could be stress-related:

_____

_____   ☐   ☐   ☐   ☐

_____

_____   ☐   ☐   ☐   ☐

• •

IMPORTANT!

Bring this list along the next time you visit your doctor. Although these symptoms may be caused or aggravated by stress, sometimes they have other causes. If any of these symptoms become severe or don't go away, be sure to have them checked by a doctor — *two* doctors, if necessary.

• •

ACTIVITY 7

THREE KINDS OF DISTRESS

Although it may seem as if you experience many different kinds of distress, there are three main kinds: the distress of daily life, distress associated with specific stages of life, and trauma.

1. Distress of Daily Life. The routine of daily living brings aggravations, frustrations, and upsets that cause distress. Everyone experiences disappointments and personality conflicts. Things go wrong in everybody's life, to a greater or lesser degree.

2. Distress Associated With Specific Stages of Life. Each stage of life has its own problems and stressors. One of the common causes of friction among people is the failure to understand and appreciate this fact. For example, a teenager whose biggest worry is fitting in with his peer group may not understand a middle-aged parent's concerns about work or money. An elderly person stressed by failing health may not understand her granddaughter's school problems.

3. Trauma. Major unexpected, unpleasant events can cause trauma — an intense feeling of distress that generally lessens only with time. A serious accident, the loss of a limb, a divorce in the family, or the death of a loved one can all cause trauma.

Turn back to Activity #1: Eustress and Distress on pages 2–5. Put a "D" beside each concern that seems like part of daily life. Put an "S" by each one you think is associated with your stage of life. Put a "T" beside each one you believe is traumatic.

DISTRESS MINIMIZERS

When you are experiencing distress, you may need time, energy, careful thought, and help from others to identify exactly what is bothering you. You may need even more time, energy, thought, and skilled help to cope with your distress.

To *cope* with a problem means to define it, confront it, and do something about it. Sometimes you aren't ready to do that right away. In the meantime, there are ways you can reduce your distress and keep functioning.

Here are some suggestions you can try. They won't make your distress go away, but they will help you feel calmer and better until you're ready to cope with it. Put a check mark by the ones you have tried in the past. Put an asterisk (*) by the ones that work well for you. Keep the other suggestions in mind to try the next time you feel confused or upset.

_____ Go to a movie, rent a video, or watch TV

_____ Make a meal for your family or friends

_____ Read a book or magazine (libraries are free!)

_____ Listen to your favorite music or radio station

_____ Play a musical instrument

_____ Take a walk or walk a dog

_____ Call, visit, or write to a friend

_____ Cry

_____ Put flowers or other plants in your room

_____ Get more sleep

_____ Eat foods that are good for you

_____ Give flowers to someone special

ACTIVITY 8

____ Paint or sketch something

____ Give your painting or sketch to someone as a gift

____ Light up your life by putting a pink light bulb in your lamp

____ Avoid negative people

____ Put posters up in your room, or replace old ones with new ones

____ Take extra care to look your best

____ Think about the things that are right in your life, instead of the things that are wrong in it

____ Buy a goldfish or two

____ Go swimming

____ Play a sport

____ Tell a joke or read a joke book

____ Avoid eating sugary foods; avoid caffeine in soft drinks, coffee, tea, and chocolate

____ Volunteer

____ Hug your pillow or stuffed animal

____ Punch your pillow or stuffed animal

____ Go fly a kite

____ Reorganize your stuff

____ Call a crisis line

____ Eat a good breakfast

____ Clean your closet, drawers, or room

____ Scream

____ Go to a support group or start one of your own

____ Smile, then smile again and again

____ Exercise

____ Take a hot bath or a cold shower

____ Keep your chin up, your shoulders back, and your stomach in

____ Paint a wall, a room, a floor, or some furniture

____ Write a letter to someone about all the things you feel, then tear it up

____ Go to an art gallery, conservatory, park, aquarium, or museum (many are free!)

____ Laugh; make someone else laugh

____ Go window shopping

____ Get a manicure, pedicure, haircut, or massage

____ Treat yourself to your favorite healthful food

____ Play or design a board game or computer game

____ Play cards

____ Put on a bright hat, shirt, underwear, or socks

____ Go to the zoo

____ People-watch and make up stories about the people you see

____ Visit someone in the hospital or in a home for senior citizens

____ Meditate

____ _____

____ _____

____ _____

ACTIVITY 9

MEDITATION AND RELAXATION

For centuries, people have studied and used yoga, meditation, and other relaxation techniques to help them deal with distress. Here are some techniques for you to try. For each, find a quiet, private place and lie down or sit comfortably. These are especially good to practice when you are trying to go to sleep.

• Close your eyes and slowly breathe in while you count to eight. Hold your breath while you count to four, then slowly let your breath out while you count to eight again. Repeat until you feel relaxed.

• Close your eyes and slowly tense up each part of your body. Start by scrunching your toes, then tense up your ankles, then your calves, and so on up to the top of your scalp. When your whole body is tense, slowly relax each muscle group from your head back down to your toes. Concentrate on how comfortable it feels to be completely relaxed.

• Close your eyes and imagine that you are lying on a beach. Pretend to feel warm sand slowly sifting over your body. Feel the warmth and comfort of it, from your toes to your neck.

• Close your eyes and count sheep, hamburgers on an assembly line, cars going around and around a track, boxcars of a never-ending train, or whatever you can think of that relaxes you.

If you'd like to learn more about yoga, meditation, and relaxation techniques, visit your library or bookstore. There are many books available on these subjects. One or more of them may hold a key to helping you deal with your distress.

Distress Maximizers

Some people deal with distress in ways that help them for short periods of time. In the long run, however, what they thought would *minimize* their distress ends up *maximizing* it, and they feel more stressed-out than ever. Sometimes their "solutions" add other more serious stressors to their lives.

On pages 22–25, you'll find a list of "distress maximizers." Read each one and think about what its long-term harmful consequences might be. Then write down one or more of these consequences.

ACTIVITY 10

1. Overeating:

_____

_____

_____

2. Not eating enough:

_____

_____

_____

3. Oversleeping:

_____

_____

_____

4. Not sleeping enough:

_____

_____

_____

5. Abusing alcohol or other drugs:

_____

_____

_____

6. Vandalism:

_____

_____

_____

7. Gambling:

_____

_____

_____

8. Throwing temper tantrums:

_____

_____

_____

9. Running away:

_____

_____

_____

10. Lying:

_____

_____

_____

11. Blaming others for things that are your fault:

_____

_____

_____

12. Being physically abusive toward other people:

_____

_____

_____

13. Being verbally abusive toward other people:

_____

_____

_____

14. Withdrawing into your own world:

_____

_____

_____

15. Stealing:

_____

_____

_____

16. Watching TV, listening to music, or playing computer games all or most of the time (to the point where it's an obsession):

_____

_____

_____

17. Manipulating other people:

_____

_____

_____

18. Changing your appearance in ways that annoy, distress, or threaten other people:

_____

_____

_____

19. Rebelling against rules at home:

_____

_____

_____

20. Rebelling against rules at school:

_____

_____

_____

21. Rebelling against society's rules:

_____

_____

_____

22. Being violent toward yourself (hurting yourself physically; attempting suicide):

_____

_____

_____

23. Hanging out instead of going to school, to work, or home:

_____

_____

_____

"Life is partly what you make it,
and partly how you take it."
Anonymous

ACTIVITY 11

THE STREAM-OF-CONSCIOUSNESS TECHNIQUE

Sometimes you may feel upset, confused, or angry without knowing why. Identifying your distressor is the first and most important step in dealing with a problem. One way to identify your distressor is with the "stream-of-consciousness" technique.

Stream of consciousness is the continuous, unedited flow of thoughts and feelings through your mind. With the stream-of-consciousness technique, you speak to someone or write down on paper whatever you are thinking and feeling.

To tap into your stream of consciousness, follow these steps:

1. If you have a trusted friend or relative who is a good listener, sit down with him or her in a private place and talk about what is on your mind. Or, if you would rather keep your thoughts and feelings to yourself, write them down. Don't worry about misspelled words, grammar, or incomplete sentences. Just write!

Some people keep a journal or diary and write in it every day. Others record their thoughts, using a tape recorder.

TIP: When keeping a stream-of-consciousness record, date each entry for future reference. Keep your entries in a private place.

2. Wait an hour, a day, a week, or a month. Give your thoughts and feelings a chance to fall into place. Sometimes problems solve themselves. And sometimes other problems come along to take their place.

Often your mind works on problems when you're not aware of it. For example, some people find solutions to their problems after a good night's sleep.

3. If you're still upset, read what you wrote or recall what you said to see if that helps you identify your problem. If you talked to someone about it, ask that person if he or she has any insights or ideas about your problem.

You may find that one thought or feeling keeps coming back. Try to pick out key words and phrases as clues to your problem.

You may have to write or record your thoughts over time to identify what is bothering you. Don't get discouraged. Keep writing or recording. A pattern may appear. Remember: The more accurately you can identify a distressor, the easier it will be to deal with.

Read the examples of stream-of-consciousness writing on page 28. Try to figure out what the person is worried about. Can you come up with any suggestions about how he or she should solve the problem?

ACTIVITY 11

DIARY ENTRY 1

March 15

He did it again! Four thousand pages of homework! Two — not one, two — history chapters to read, and sixteen — count 'em! — SIXTEEN questions to answer and when is it due? tomorrow! There's no way…Why should I bother — I'll only get another D anyway. Who does he think he is, anyway? No wonder all the kids hate him. Doesn't he know other teachers give homework too? As if the whole world cares about those stupid Ancient Greeks one little bit — not likely! They've been dead for three thousand years…

1. What is the writer's problem?

_____

_____

_____

2. What do you think the writer should do?

_____

_____

_____

DIARY ENTRY 2

August 12

I'm soooooo tired. My head aches and I wish I was anywhere else but here. Whenever they fight I can't sleep — all I can do is watch TV and eat junk food. Great! now I'll be even fatter and uglier than ever. I wish I had someone who would get me out of here but who'd look at a pig like me anyway? If this yelling goes on much longer I'll go crazy…

1. What is the writer's problem?

_____

_____

_____

2. What do you think the writer should do?

_____

_____

_____

Practice using the stream-of-consciousness technique to identify distressors in your life.

Date: _____

_____

_____

_____

_____

_____

_____

_____

_____

_____

_____

_____

_____

_____

_____

_____

_____

_____

_____

_____

_____

_____

_____

_____

ACTIVITY 12

ARE YOU SPINNING YOUR WHEELS?

The circle is a symbol of balance, harmony, and peace. Distress can make you feel off balance, out of tune, or at war with the world around you.

Imagine your life as a wheel, with spokes dividing it into different sections according to how important they are.

**HOW MY LIFE
LOOKS NOW**

If you experience routine distress, your life may look like this…

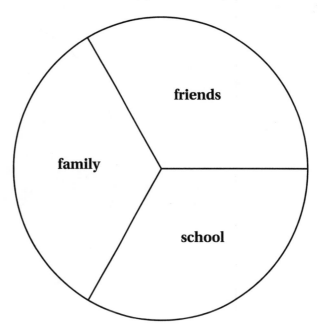

**HOW I'D LIKE MY
LIFE TO LOOK**

…when you'd like it to look like this…

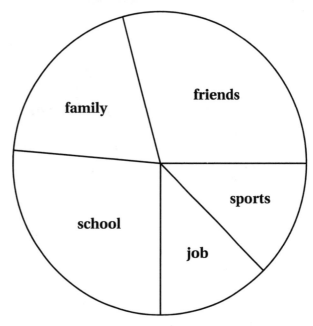

ACTIVITY 12

**HOW MY LIFE
LOOKS NOW**

If you're having problems with school, your life may look like this…

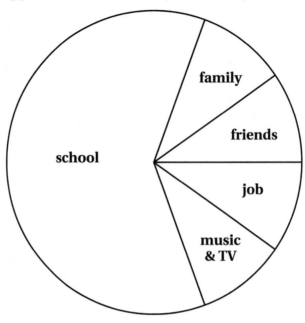

**HOW I'D LIKE MY
LIFE TO LOOK**

…when you'd like it to look like this…

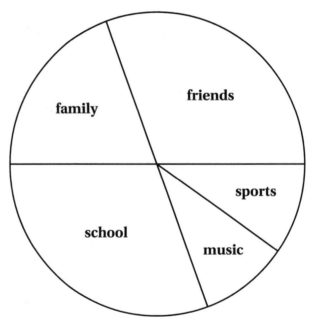

**HOW MY LIFE
LOOKS NOW**

If your family is having problems, your life may look like this...

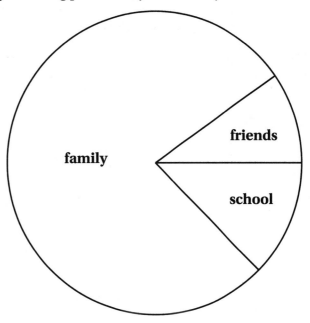

**HOW I'D LIKE MY
LIFE TO LOOK**

...when you'd like it to look like this...

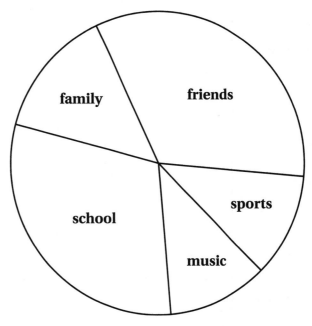

ACTIVITY 12

Think of how your life looks now, and how you'd like it to look. Then complete your own "stress wheels" by dividing these into sections and labeling each section.

HOW MY LIFE LOOKS NOW

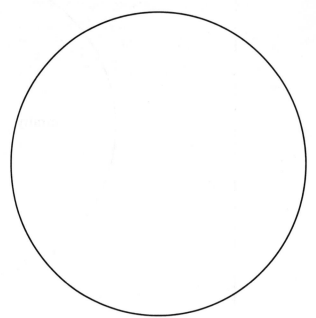

HOW I'D LIKE MY LIFE TO LOOK

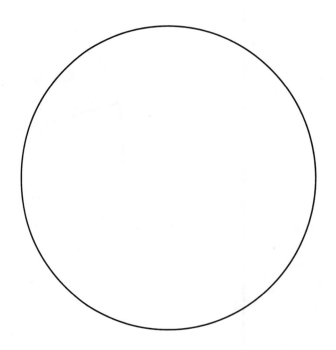

In labeling the parts of your life, have you identified a part that seems too large? YES ☐ NO ☐

Would making it smaller make you happier? YES ☐ NO ☐

Why or why not?

_____

_____

_____

Is there anything you can do to make it smaller?

_____

_____

_____

Have you identified a part of your life that seems too small?
YES ☐ NO ☐

Would making it larger make you happier? YES ☐ NO ☐

Why or why not?

_____

_____

_____

Is there anything you can do to make it larger?

_____

_____

_____

ACTIVITY 13

What's your problem?

If you're going to spend a lot of time and energy dealing with a problem, you first need to know what the problem really is. This takes step-by-step detective work — like this:

Step One: State your problem.

Step Two: State your problem more specifically.

Step Three: State your problem precisely.

The best way to get from Step One to Step Two, and from Step Two to Step Three, is by asking yourself some hard questions — and giving honest answers.

Here are three examples of this process in action.

Step One: The Problem: "I'm angry at my father."

- Is the problem your father, or is it the way he treats your family?

- Is it the way he treats you?

- Is it that he doesn't give you the time, attention, or money you feel you need?

Step Two: More Specifically: "My father doesn't pay enough attention to me."

- Who does he pay attention to?

- Does it seem that he pays more attention to someone else in the family — like your little brother?

Step Three: Precisely: "My father seems to prefer my little brother, and I feel neglected."

Step One: The Problem: "I'm mad at my teacher."

- Is the problem your teacher, or is it that the subject she teaches is very difficult for you?

- Is it that you need extra help?

- Is it that you don't want to ask for extra help?

Step Two: More Specifically: "I'm afraid to ask for the extra help I need to do the work."

- What would happen if you asked for help?

- Would you have to work harder?

Step Three: Precisely: "If I ask for help, I'll have to make a big effort to improve, and I'm not sure I want to do that."

Step One: The Problem: "I need more money."

- Is the problem that you don't have enough money, or that you don't make good decisions about the money you have?

- Is it that you mismanage your money?

Step Two: More Specifically: "I don't manage my money very well."

- Do you spend your money foolishly?

- Or do you buy things you can't afford, meaning you never have any money left over for other things you want or need?

Step Three: Precisely: "I never have any money because I try to keep up with friends and trends I can't afford. I have a hard time accepting my standard of living."

ACTIVITY 13

Now that you know how this three-step process works, try using it to define real problems in your life.

Step One: My Problem:

_____

_____

_____

Step Two: More Specifically:

_____

_____

_____

Step Three: Precisely:

_____

_____

_____

Step One: My Problem:

_____

_____

_____

Step Two: More Specifically:

_____

_____

_____

Step Three: Precisely:

_____

_____

_____

Step One: My Problem:

_____

_____

_____

Step Two: More Specifically:

_____

_____

_____

Step Three: Precisely:

_____

_____

_____

Something to think about

Precise may not be nice, so people sometimes avoid thinking about their problems or trying to come up with solutions. It can hurt to be completely honest with yourself about your motives, actions, expectations, or attitudes. Just remember that most problems won't go away by themselves. Ignoring them can hurt you even more in the long run.

ACTIVITY 14

CHOOSING SOLUTIONS

Your life is a series of choices. You decide when to get out of bed, what to wear, what to eat for breakfast, and so on throughout your day. Many of these choices are automatic and based on your daily routine.

Choices about problems are different. Most problems aren't routine, so the choices about them aren't automatic. You must think about what you will choose and why. These are conscious, deliberate decisions.

Choosing (or not choosing) can be a source of distress all by itself. Here are three reasons why:

• You can choose only from among the possible solutions you're aware of. Yet you know that other solutions must exist somewhere in the world…What if one of those is better than the one you choose?

• You may be able to anticipate the consequences of each of your possible solutions. But you can never be sure of them until after you've made your choice.

• You may feel too upset, depressed, confused, or overwhelmed to make any choice, let alone the best choice.

Still, there will be times when you *must* make a choice — there's no way around it! Recognize the risks and try to anticipate the consequences. Then make your choice and take responsibility for the outcome — good or bad.

REMEMBER…

Your life is a series of choices.
You always have the power to choose in some way.
NOT CHOOSING IS A CHOICE.

Sometimes having to choose may seem overwhelming. It helps to know that there are three basic types of choices, and that with most problems, you will be facing only one type.

1. A clear-cut choice. This is one of the simplest choices to make. One option is clearly better than another.

For example: You have to choose between getting a puppy or getting a kitten. You don't like cats, so it's a simple decision to choose the puppy.

Or: You have to choose between buying a purple sweater or buying a black one. You love purple, so it's a simple decision to choose the purple sweater.

2. A "win-win" situation. This choice is a bit harder to make. Both of your options look good, but you aren't sure which one you prefer.

For example: You have to choose between apple pie or lemon meringue. You love both kinds.

Or: You have to choose between playing soccer or playing baseball. You enjoy both, and you're equally good at both.

With a "win-win" situation, you can't lose! But neither can you have or do everything you want. You still have to make a decision.

3. The double bind. This choice is the most difficult to make. None of your options is what you really want, but you have to choose one anyway. You must try to figure out which choice will be the least distressing.

For example: You have to choose between doing your math homework first or your history homework first. You'd rather do neither. You may as well flip a coin and get on with it rather than waste your time and energy trying to choose between them.

ACTIVITY 14

Describe three clear-cut choices you have had to make.

a. _____

_____

b. _____

_____

c. _____

_____

Describe three win-win choices you have had to make.

a. _____

_____

b. _____

_____

c. _____

_____

Describe three double-bind choices you have had to make.

a. _____

_____

b. _____

_____

c. _____

_____

Twelve Distressing Myths

Psychologist Albert Ellis says that people get worried and upset because of the way they interpret their stressors. He believes that people can choose to react *rationally* (reasonably) or *irrationally* (unreasonably) to a stressor.

Dr. Ellis has identified twelve *myths* (irrational beliefs) that people commonly cling to, even though these beliefs make them unhappy. You'll find these myths on pages 44–46. Read each one, then tell if you agree or disagree with it. Explain your answer.

ACTIVITY 15

MYTH 1

You must be loved by everyone, and everyone must love everything you do.

AGREE _____ DISAGREE _____

WHY? _____

_____

_____

MYTH 2

You must be intelligent, competent, and capable in everything you do.

AGREE _____ DISAGREE _____

WHY? _____

_____

_____

MYTH 3

Some things in the world are bad, wrong, or evil, and you must be punished severely if you see, do, think, or feel them.

AGREE _____ DISAGREE _____

WHY? _____

_____

_____

MYTH 4

The world is over when things don't turn out the way you want them to.

AGREE _____ DISAGREE _____

WHY? _____

_____

_____

MYTH 5

You have no control over your own happiness. Your happiness depends on what happens to you.

AGREE _____   DISAGREE _____

WHY? _____

_____

_____

MYTH 6

Worrying about something bad keeps it from happening.

AGREE _____   DISAGREE _____

WHY? _____

_____

_____

MYTH 7

It's always easier to run away from problems than it is to deal with them.

AGREE _____   DISAGREE _____

WHY? _____

_____

_____

MYTH 8

You need someone else to depend on. You can't function independently.

AGREE _____   DISAGREE _____

WHY? _____

_____

_____

ACTIVITY 15

MYTH 9

If something bad happened in your past, it must affect you forever.

AGREE _____ DISAGREE _____

WHY? _____

_____

_____

MYTH 10

If someone else doesn't live his or her life in the way you think he or she should, you must do everything you can to change that person.

AGREE _____ DISAGREE _____

WHY? _____

_____

_____

MYTH 11

There is only one correct answer to any problem. If that answer isn't found, the consequences will be terrible.

AGREE _____ DISAGREE _____

WHY? _____

_____

_____

MYTH 12

You can't help feeling the way you do.

AGREE _____ DISAGREE _____

WHY? _____

_____

_____

"I wear the chain I forged in life."
Jacob Marley in A Christmas
Carol *by Charles Dickens*

WHEN THE PROBLEM ISN'T YOURS

Researchers have found that one of the most distressing things about some problems isn't the problem itself, but the feeling that you have no control over it. Most often, you feel this way when the problem isn't your problem, but you are feeling the effects of someone else's problem. Perhaps someone has failed to live up to a responsibility, and that affects you. Maybe someone treated you unfairly or hurt you on purpose.

For example: If your parents are having trouble in their relationship, their behavior may distress you. Although *their* relationship is *their* business, how they relate to you is your business. You are powerless to solve their problems for them, but you do have some control over how they relate to you.

Or: If your family is having money problems, you may be unhappy. But the responsibility for solving these problems lies with your parents, not with you. Even though you may try to help by doing without some things you want, by finding work, or by making things you need, you are powerless to solve your family's money problems.

Realizing and accepting that someone else's problem isn't yours to solve can take some of the pressure off you. (Another way to reduce your distress is by using some of the suggestions listed in Activity #8: Distress Minimizers on pages 17–19.)

ACTIVITY 16

Try to think of three problems you have no control over. For each one, think of ways to help yourself feel better, even though you're powerless to solve the problem.

1. A problem I have no control over is:

_____

_____

I can help myself feel better anyway by:

_____

_____

2. A problem I have no control over is:

_____

_____

I can help myself feel better anyway by:

_____

_____

3. A problem I have no control over is:

_____

_____

I can help myself feel better anyway by:

_____

_____

No one is ever in a position of total control. Much in our lives depends upon other peoples' actions and attitudes, chance events, and luck.

Something to think about

WHY PEOPLE POSTPONE PROBLEM SOLVING 1: FEAR OF MAKING A MISTAKE

Why don't people just make up their minds to solve their problems and move on? Many people do just that. But others put off solving problems for a number of reasons. One common reason is the fear of making a mistake.

Because mistakes can cause pain, most people don't make them on purpose. When they find themselves in a problem situation, they just make the best choice they can, based on the information they have. If their choice turns out to be a mistake, it's usually not because they wanted it to be.

Have you ever postponed making a choice because you were afraid of making a mistake? The guidelines on page 50 can help you feel stronger and safer about your choices.

ACTIVITY 17

You make your best choices when...

...you have gathered all the reliable information you can about the choices you have,

...you have thought of all the options there are to choose from,

...you have considered both the short-term and the long-term consequences of each option,

...you are prepared to accept the responsibility for your choice, and

...your choice feels right to you.

You make your worst choices when...

...you base your choice on unreliable or incomplete information,

...you don't know about all the options available to you, or you choose to ignore some of those options,

...you don't consider the short-term and long-term consequences of your choice,

...you refuse to accept the responsibility for your choice, and

...your choice doesn't feel right to you.

Remember: Every time you take control of your problem, make a good choice, or solve a problem successfully, you gain experience. This increases the likelihood that you will take control, make a good choice, or solve a problem successfully in the future.

When you are faced with an important decision, who do you turn to for good advice and reliable information? List as many people (or sources) as you can.

_____

_____

_____

_____

_____

How do you know when the information someone gives you (or you find for yourself) is reliable and complete?

_____

_____

_____

_____

_____

Have you ever learned, *after* making a decision, that you acted on information that was unreliable or incomplete? YES ☐ NO ☐

What happened?

_____

_____

_____

_____

"That which doesn't destroy me makes me strong."
Anonymous

ACTIVITY 18

WHAT'S GOOD ABOUT A MISTAKE?

1927: Frank Epperson, lemonade salesman, accidentally leaves a glass half full of lemonade on a window sill. Overnight, the weather turns cold and the lemonade, with a spoon stuck in it, freezes. The next morning Epperson realizes he has invented the Popsicle.

1949: A scientist is trying to create a synthetic rubber when he accidentally drops boric acid into silicone oil. Paul Hodgson buys the stretchy, bouncy stuff and calls it Silly Putty.

Ignore the facts, follow your feelings, and you may make some of your best — and worst — choices. If you do make the wrong choice, try to learn as much as you can from your mistake. It may take time, money, hard work, and determination to get back on track, but many mistakes can be corrected.

It helps to know that most people have made at least one big, fat, juicy mistake. It also helps to know that a mistake can lead to long-term benefits. Many wonderful discoveries, important inventions, and new relationships have resulted from mistakes.

What are some mistakes you've made that you've learned from? List as many as you can.

_____

_____

_____

_____

_____

_____

What are some mistakes you've made that have had positive results in the end? List as many as you can.

_____

_____

_____

_____

_____

_____

"Success is the fine art of making mistakes when nobody's looking."
Anonymous

ARE THERE REALLY PERFECT PEOPLE IN THE WORLD?

Many people pass themselves off as "perfect." They act as if they've never made a mistake in their lives. In fact, *everybody* makes mistakes — *nobody* is perfect.

1

Have you ever pretended to be perfect? YES ☐ NO ☐

If yes, when?

_____

_____

Why?

_____

_____

Was pretending to be perfect worth the effort? YES ☐ NO ☐

Explain your answer:

_____

_____

Do you know anyone who is perfect? YES ☐ NO ☐

If yes, who? _____

What makes you think that person is perfect?

_____

_____

Does that person think that he or she is perfect? YES ☐ NO ☐

How can you tell?

_____

_____

Do other people think that he or she is perfect? YES ☐ NO ☐

How can you tell?

_____

_____

Why do you think people pretend to be perfect? List as many reasons as you can think of.

_____

_____

_____

_____

_____

_____

_____

_____

_____

Did you think of these?

Did you think of these reasons why people pretend to be perfect?

• Because it hurts to remember mistakes, and it's embarrassing to let other people know about them.

• Because people like to hide their weaknesses so others won't think they are fools and take advantage of them.

• Because letting other people know about their mistakes means admitting the mistakes to themselves — something they may not have done before.

• Because they're afraid that if they're not perfect, others won't take their advice or listen to their wisdom. (Some people want you to just "accept" that they're wise instead of telling you how they got that way. Wisdom comes from experience — and experience includes mistakes.)

• Because they believe in the Twelve Distressing Myths (see Activity #15, pages 44–46).

Advice: The wise don't need it, and fools won't heed it.

Something to think about

HOW OTHERS HAVE HANDLED MISTAKES

Do you know an adult (parent, teacher, or neighbor) who will talk to you honestly about a serious mistake he or she has made? Ask around until you find one or two who will. Then arrange to "interview" each person.

• •

IMPORTANT!

Remember to be responsible about respecting the confidentiality of the people you interview.

• •

ACTIVITY 20

INTERVIEW 1

1. What was the mistake you made?

_____

_____

_____

2. Did you try to correct your mistake? YES ☐ NO ☐

Why or why not?

_____

_____

_____

3. If you did try to correct your mistake, what did you do?

_____

_____

_____

4. Did your mistake have any long-term consequences? YES ☐ NO ☐

If yes, what were they?

_____

_____

_____

5. Did your mistake have any long-term benefits? YES ☐ NO ☐

If yes, what were they?

_____

_____

_____

6. What did you learn from your mistake?

_____

_____

_____

7. Would you make the same mistake again, knowing only what you knew then? YES ☐ NO ☐

Why or why not?

_____

_____

_____

8. Would you make the same mistake again, knowing what you know now? YES ☐ NO ☐

Why or why not?

_____

_____

_____

When you are finished doing the interview, ask yourself this question:

Now that you have had this discussion with an adult, would you make the same mistake he or she did, or one like it? YES ☐ NO ☐

Why or why not?

_____

_____

_____

ACTIVITY 20

INTERVIEW 2

1. What was the mistake you made?

_____

_____

_____

2. Did you try to correct your mistake? YES ☐ NO ☐

Why or why not?

_____

_____

_____

3. If you did try to correct your mistake, what did you do?

_____

_____

_____

4. Did your mistake have any long-term consequences? YES ☐ NO ☐

If yes, what were they?

_____

_____

_____

5. Did your mistake have any long-term benefits? YES ☐ NO ☐

If yes, what were they?

_____

_____

_____

6. What did you learn from your mistake?

_____

_____

_____

7. Would you make the same mistake again, knowing only what you knew then? YES ☐ NO ☐

Why or why not?

_____

_____

_____

8. Would you make the same mistake again, knowing what you know now? YES ☐ NO ☐

Why or why not?

_____

_____

_____

When you are finished doing the interview, ask yourself this question:

Now that you have had this discussion with an adult, would you make the same mistake he or she did, or one like it? YES ☐ NO ☐

Why or why not?

_____

_____

_____

"The moment may be temporary, but the memory is forever."
Bud Mayer

WHY PEOPLE POSTPONE PROBLEM SOLVING 2: FEAR OF BEING HURT, LOSING LOVE, OR HURTING OTHERS

No pain, no gain.

Athletes use this saying to describe how choosing a painful course of action can lead to great rewards. In deciding how hard and how long they must train, athletes weigh the pain of hard work, perseverance, self-discipline, and personal sacrifice against their future achievements.

You may find it helpful to use this ratio — pain to gain — when making decisions in your life. Is it worth it to bear hurtful feelings (shame, guilt, rejection, isolation) if that's what it takes to solve a problem? The keys to this idea are *degree* and *duration*. How much pain? For how long? For how much success?

Has there ever been a time when solving a problem or achieving a goal caused you pain? YES ☐ NO ☐

If yes, tell what happened:

_____

_____

_____

Was the gain worth the pain? YES ☐ NO ☐

Why or why not?

_____

_____

_____

Has there ever been a time when you caused pain to someone else by solving a problem or achieving a goal? YES ☐ NO ☐

If yes, tell what happened:

_____

_____

_____

Was the gain worth the pain? YES ☐ NO ☐

Why or why not?

_____

_____

_____

ACTIVITY 21

Has there ever been a time when someone prevented you from solving a problem or achieving a goal through "emotional blackmail" (for example, by threatening to hurt your feelings, reject you, humiliate you, or make you feel guilty)? YES ☐ NO ☐

If yes, tell what happened:

_____

_____

_____

Was the gain worth the pain? YES ☐ NO ☐

Why or why not?

_____

_____

_____

What could you do if someone tries to do this to you again?

_____

_____

_____

_____

_____

_____

WHY PEOPLE POSTPONE PROBLEM SOLVING 3: FEAR OF RISK/ FEAR OF CHANGE

Are you comfortable with your daily habits or your patterns of thinking, believing, feeling, or behaving? If you are, then you may not want to risk changing them, unless the reward is great or almost guaranteed.

Many people settle for being safe rather than experience the distress (and eustress) of risk-taking, creative change, and personal growth. They feel most secure when they stick to their routines. Their *security habits* are good enough for them.

ACTIVITY 22

Describe the security habits you see in the people around you.

_____

_____

_____

_____

_____

What security habits do you see in yourself?

_____

_____

_____

_____

_____

Think of rewards or goals you'd like to achieve. What risks do you think you would take to reach them?

REWARD/GOAL   RISK

a. _____   _____

b. _____   _____

c. _____   _____

d. _____   _____

e. _____   _____

"If you want a place in the sun,
you have to expect some blisters."
Rotator

Why People Postpone Problem Solving 4: Fear of Being Held Responsible

Some people are reluctant to accept responsibility, especially for making difficult decisions and resolving serious problems. A mature person accepts responsibility for his or her decisions, and accepts the consequences of his or her actions.

• If you make a decision that fails, don't *rationalize* (make excuses for) your failure. Admit your mistake, learn from it, and move on.

• If you're unhappy with your decision, don't blame others. Tell yourself you'll do better next time.

• If your decision creates even more problems, don't expect other people to solve them. Do it yourself! Do everything you can to make things right!

ACTIVITY 23

Do you know someone who seems immature when it comes to taking responsibility for his or her decisions? YES ☐ NO ☐

Why do you think he or she acts that way?

_____

_____

_____

Has there ever been a time when you acted in a mature way while others didn't? YES ☐ NO ☐

If yes, tell what happened:

_____

_____

_____

Was it hard to act responsibly? YES ☐ NO ☐

Why or why not?

_____

_____

_____

"You're only young once,
but you can be immature forever."
Anonymous

WHY PEOPLE POSTPONE PROBLEM SOLVING 5: FEAR OF RESOLVING THE PROBLEM

Sometimes people avoid solving a problem, even when they have the time, money, energy, and/or skill to solve it. Sometimes people avoid solving a problem even when they know their best choices and feel reasonably certain about the consequences.

Why? Perhaps they aren't ready to solve the problem. Perhaps they are being emotionally blackmailed by someone. Perhaps they have learned to be helpless. Perhaps they like having problems because they get a lot of attention and/or sympathy from other people. Perhaps solving their problem will result in a lifestyle change or a new role they're not willing to accept.

ACTIVITY 24

Has there ever been a time when you put off solving a problem because you were afraid to solve it? YES ☐ NO ☐

If yes, what were you really afraid of?

_____

_____

_____

Did waiting help or hurt? HELP ☐ HURT ☐

Explain your answer:

_____

_____

_____

If you're faced with the same problem again someday, will you put off solving it? YES ☐ NO ☐

Why or why not?

_____

_____

_____

"A person who aims at nothing is sure to hit it."
Anonymous

KEEPING PROBLEMS IN PERSPECTIVE

The next time a problem seems too big to solve, keep these points in mind:

• *You're not alone.* Somebody, somewhere, has experienced the problem you're facing.

• *You're getting better.* The longer you live, the more experience you'll have in dealing with people, situations, and events. Problem solving will become more routine for you. It will get easier!

• *You may be better off than someone else.* Your problem, no matter what it is, is probably smaller than someone else's problem.

• *You can still take good care of yourself.* Even though you have a problem that's bothering you, you can eat right, exercise, get enough sleep, even treat yourself to your favorite things.

• *You can ask yourself these questions:*

"In ten years, will I still have this problem?"

"In ten years, will this problem have made a big difference in my life?"

• *You can get help.* Is there anyone who can help you solve your problem? If yes, what are you waiting for?

• *You can use a chart to map out your problem.* A flowchart, for example, is like a picture with arrows pointing the way from a problem to possible solutions. Sometimes writing down everything you know about a problem, and the choices you have, can make things much more clear. When in doubt, put it in writing!

ACTIVITY 25

Here is a flowchart you can use to map out your problem.

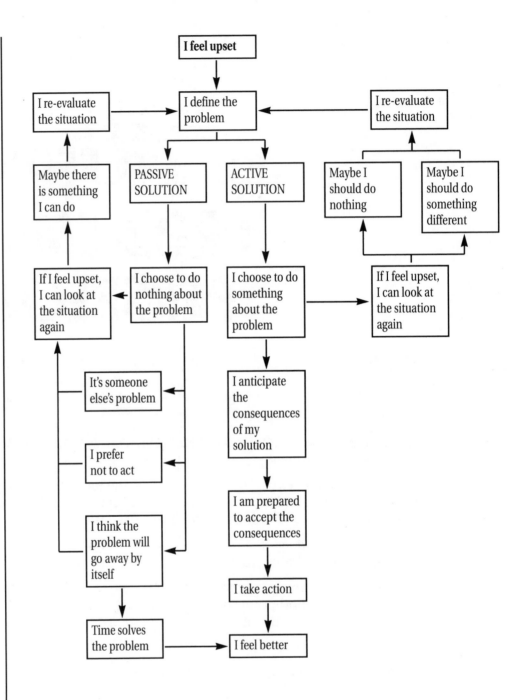

Here is a maze you can use to puzzle your way through your problem.

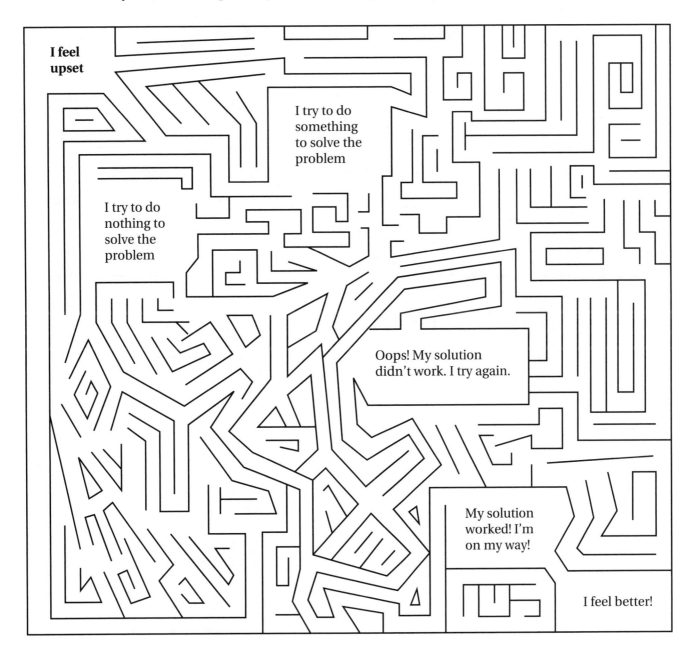

ACTIVITY 25

Use this diagram to solve a real problem.

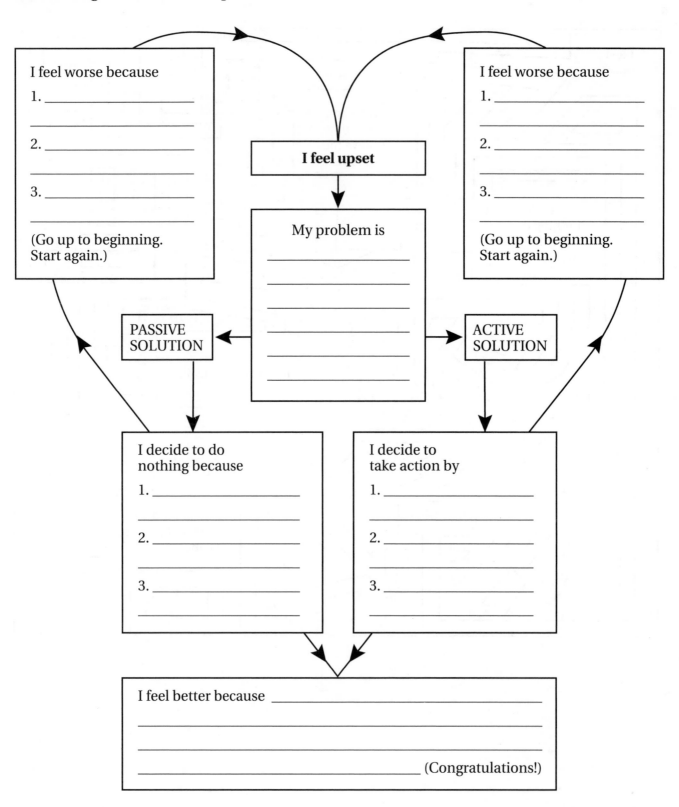

I feel worse because

1. _____

_____

2. _____

_____

3. _____

_____

(Go up to beginning. Start again.)

I feel upset

My problem is

_____

_____

_____

_____

_____

_____

I feel worse because

1. _____

_____

2. _____

_____

3. _____

_____

(Go up to beginning. Start again.)

PASSIVE SOLUTION

ACTIVE SOLUTION

I decide to do nothing because

1. _____

_____

2. _____

_____

3. _____

_____

I decide to take action by

1. _____

_____

2. _____

_____

3. _____

_____

I feel better because _____

_____

_____

_____ (Congratulations!)

Use this space to design a problem-solving diagram that works best for you. Use a real problem.

PROBLEM-SOLVING STRATEGY 1: ORGANIZE

"A journey of a thousand miles begins with a single step."
Anonymous

There's something you want to do, have, or become — but you don't know where to start. You've got a problem!

One effective way to approach problem solving is by organizing your thoughts into a plan of action. Here is one way to do this:

1. State your goal very clearly to yourself. Write it down as a simple, clear statement. List several reasons why it would be good for you to do, have, or become whatever it is you want.

2. Decide how realistic your goal is. How much time, effort, skill, money, and determination are you ready to invest? What sacrifices are you willing to make?

3. Re-state your goal in a positive way: "I will…." Indicate when you expect to achieve that goal.

4. Remember that goals are achieved one step at a time. The smaller the steps, the greater your chance of success. Decide on a sequence of steps that will give you a series of small successes as you move toward your long-range goal.

5. Pause now and then to make sure you're still on the right track. Does your long-range goal need to be redefined? Are you keeping to the time line you have set out for yourself?

EXAMPLE

Let's say you want a bike. Having a bike would be good for you because you could get around easier and not have to ask other people for rides all the time. Plus you could get a paper route and earn extra money.

Reading from bottom (stating the problem) to top (achieving your goal), here's one way you might go about getting your bike:

10.
Squirrel
away
enough
money! Make
purchase!

---

9. Give up one
movie a month. Put
money saved into your
account. Enter it
on your chart.

---

8. Branch out. Get a job(s)
— paper route, babysit, run
errands for neighbors — and put
all money earned into your bank
account. Enter it on your chart.

---

7. Decide to store away half your
allowance in the bank each week to save
for your purchase.

---

6. Make a chart to graph how close you are to
achieving your goal. Mark in the amount each
time you add to your bank account. Look at it
every day.

---

5. Open a savings account at the bank and put in as
much money as you can. Figure out how much more
money you need.

---

4. Find out how much money you will need.

---

3. Stop being a sap. Accept that you must earn the money for
your purchase yourself.

---

2. BEG your parents for money. (Get refused.)

---

1. Needle your parents for money. (Get refused.)

**Start Here at the
Root of the Problem**

ACTIVITY 26

Now *you* try it. Think of a long-range goal you'd like to achieve. Starting from the bottom, work your way up by listing the steps you will take to achieve it.

MY ACHIEVEMENT: _____

10. _____

9. _____

8. _____

7. _____

6. _____

5. _____

4. _____

3. _____

2. _____

1. _____

MY GOAL:

_____

_____

PROBLEM-SOLVING STRATEGY 2: DON'T LET YOUR PROBLEM OVERWHELM YOU

Sometimes a problem can seem overwhelming. You don't know what to do or where to start.

At times like these…relax. Take a deep breath. Then take a look at the problem-solving guidelines on page 80. Put a check mark by the ones you have tried in the past. Put an asterisk (*) by the ones that work well for you. Keep the other guidelines in mind to try the next time you feel overwhelmed by a problem.

ACTIVITY 27

To begin:

____ Plunge in. Start anywhere — just start! Do any task at all. When it's done, you'll have fewer tasks to do.

____ Do the biggest, toughest task first. The rest will be a piece of cake.

____ Do the easiest tasks first. Once you've cleared a few simple tasks out of the way, you may feel more confident about tackling the bigger ones.

____ If time is important, do the most urgent task first. Then do the second most urgent task, the third most urgent task, and so on until you're done.

To keep going:

____ Encourage yourself with praise and positive self-talk from beginning to end. (For tips, see Activity #37: Problem-Solving Strategy 12: Positive Self-Talk, pages 110–112.)

____ Rest and reward yourself whenever you complete a sub-task.

____ Do your best so you can be proud of your effort.

____ When the whole task is done, CELEBRATE!

PROBLEM-SOLVING STRATEGY 3: TAKE A NEW VIEW

When facing a difficult problem, it helps to look at it from a variety of viewpoints. Taking a step back and studying the problem from a different angle can give you new insights — and perhaps suggest a solution.

To practice this problem-solving strategy, imagine each of the scenes described on pages 82–84. Then consider it from each new view.

ACTIVITY 28

An extremely messy kitchen. All the dishes and silverware have been used and left dirty on the counter and table. Spilled milk, crumbs, and sticky food are everywhere. There's no food fit to eat in the refrigerator, on the stove, or in the cupboards.

How would you view this scene if you were…

a. someone who came home starving and eager to make yourself a snack?

_____

_____

_____

b. the person who feels responsible for keeping the kitchen clean?

_____

_____

_____

c. a guest, visiting for the first time, who expects to be offered something to eat or drink?

_____

_____

_____

d. the family pet?

_____

_____

_____

A busy restaurant. There's a meal sitting under a heat lamp, waiting to be served — and it's been sitting there for at least ten minutes.

How would you view this scene if you were…

a. a hungry customer, and you knew the meal was yours?

_____

_____

_____

b. the server who took the customer's order, but who also had a dozen more tables full of hungry, angry customers?

_____

_____

_____

c. the cook who prepared the meal, taking special care to please the customer?

_____

_____

_____

d. the restaurant manager, worried about losing your job because the customer, who happens to be the owner, is expecting his lunch right away?

_____

_____

_____

ACTIVITY 28

It's report-card time — and a certain student's report card has just come home, covered with F's.

How would you view this scene if you were...

a. the student, and you knew you had tried your best?

_____

_____

_____

b. the student, and you knew you hadn't tried at all in any of your courses?

_____

_____

_____

c. a teacher who has spent extra time helping the student?

_____

_____

_____

d. the student's parent, and you really value education?

_____

_____

_____

PROBLEM-SOLVING STRATEGY 4: ROLE-PLAYING

Role-playing is an excellent problem-solving strategy. You can role-play with another person, or with a group.

When you role-play, you act out a scene that shows you dealing with a problem in a number of ways. If you find a solution that feels right to you, try acting it out in real life.

When you role-play, there are no limits to what you can try. You can take your time and discover your own best solution. Nobody is putting pressure on you to choose one solution over another.

On page 86, you'll find an example of how role-playing can help you to solve a problem. Imagine yourself in the Worst, Best, and Most Likely scenarios described.

On pages 87–89, you'll find more scenes to imagine yourself in. For these, you'll need to come up with your own descriptions for the Worst, Best, and Most Likely scenarios. Role-play the scenes with a friend or two. Switch parts and role-play them again. Feel free to ad-lib.

ACTIVITY 29

You're sitting in the audience in your school auditorium, hoping to be called up to the stage to accept a trophy you've worked hard to earn. All of your friends expect you to win it, too. The announcer gets ready to make the presentation. A hush falls over the crowd. Then the name of the winner is called…and it's your worst enemy!

THE WORST SCENARIO

I leap up and shout, "There's got to be a mistake! That's MY trophy! I earned it! It's MINE, MINE, MINE!"

Everyone stares at me in disbelief, and I burst into tears.

THE BEST SCENARIO

I'm shocked, disappointed, and hurt. Everyone turns to look at me to see how I will react. I take a deep breath, smile warmly…and lead the applause. My friends take their cue from me and join in. I can sense that they think I should have won, and I feel good about their unspoken support.

When the ceremony is over, everyone wants to shake my hand, hug me, and slap me on the back. Before they crowd around me too closely, I make my way over to my enemy, who is standing alone with the prize, and offer my sincere congratulations. I know that I will win many other honors in my life.

THE MOST LIKELY SCENARIO

I'm stunned. I can't believe my ears and eyes as my enemy goes up to claim *my* trophy. Everyone around me is clapping enthusiastically, so I try to clap, too. The ceremony ends quickly, and I stand up, feeling as if I'm in a dream. I'm swept out of the theater by the loud, noisy crowd. The shock wears off later, when I'm alone.

1

You're at a party with your friends, having a good time, when who should walk in but…your ex-boyfriend and his new girlfriend! (Or your ex-girlfriend and her new boyfriend.)

THE WORST SCENARIO

_____

_____

_____

_____

_____

_____

THE BEST SCENARIO

_____

_____

_____

_____

_____

_____

THE MOST LIKELY SCENARIO

_____

_____

_____

_____

_____

_____

ACTIVITY 29

You borrowed your friend's basketball. You promised to take really good care of it, but you left it at the park by mistake — and when you went back, it was gone. Your friend has asked you to return the basketball — now!

THE WORST SCENARIO

_____

_____

_____

_____

_____

_____

THE BEST SCENARIO

_____

_____

_____

_____

_____

_____

THE MOST LIKELY SCENARIO

_____

_____

_____

_____

_____

_____

One of your friends is acting crazy. You and your best friend are trying to calm him, but the harder you try, the crazier he gets. Suddenly the situation gets out of hand, and your crazy friend knocks your best friend to the ground. Your best friend doesn't move.

THE WORST SCENARIO

_____

_____

_____

_____

_____

_____

THE BEST SCENARIO

_____

_____

_____

_____

_____

_____

THE MOST LIKELY SCENARIO

_____

_____

_____

_____

_____

_____

PROBLEM-SOLVING STRATEGY 5: BREAK YOUR DISTRESS HABIT

Some people have recurring dreams — dreams they keep having over and over. Other people have recurring stressors — stressors that keep coming back.

Do you have a recurring stressor? Do you automatically respond the same way every time it returns?

For example: Your older sister teases you constantly. She knows that you'll respond by getting mad, shouting, and slapping her (your stress habit), giving her an excuse to slap you back.

You can break your distress habit. You can control your response and change it. You can decide to ignore the stressor in the future. Or you can think of a different response, one that may make the stressor go away for good.

There are many different ways to break your distress habit. You can ignore the teasing, walk away, go to your room, phone your parent at work, go jogging, smile, give your sister a compliment or a gift you have made — *anything* but respond in your usual way.

Another example may be that you always get distress symptoms (clammy hands, rapid heartbeat, shortness of breath) whenever you have to speak or perform in front of people. You can try to break your distress habit with some of the techniques described in Activity #9: Meditation and Relaxation, on page 20.

If you have a recurring stressor, you can also choose to do nothing — at least for a little while. You can substitute an easy problem for a hard one. Some students do their easiest homework before tackling their hardest assignments. Some adults overwork to avoid the problems in their family life.

1. Think of a recurring distressor in your life. How do you usually respond to it?

_____

_____

_____

2. What usually happens when you respond to your distressor in the same old way?

_____

_____

_____

3. What are some ways you could change your usual response?

_____

_____

_____

_____

_____

4. Would regular use of a new response to the recurring distressor break your distress habit? YES ☐ NO ☐

Why or why not?

_____

_____

_____

"A habit cannot be tossed out the window;
it must be coaxed down the stairs a step at a time."
Mark Twain

PROBLEM-SOLVING STRATEGY 6: IS IT *REALLY* SO BAD?

You have a problem that's bothering you a lot. It takes up all of your time, energy, and thought. It's a very serious problem!

But how serious is it *really?* Think about it. Compare it to the problems other people have. This doesn't mean that your problem isn't important to you. But someone, somewhere, is probably feeling worse than you are right now. Resist the temptation to be jealous of people who seem "better off" than you are. Think about those who are *worse* off.

List five problems you are glad you don't have:

1. _____

2. _____

3. _____

4. _____

5. _____

Something to think about
Many people make themselves happier by helping less fortunate people. Will you? If you will, then how? When?

Problem-Solving Strategy 7: Get Help When You Really Need It

When you were much younger, you probably had help solving many of your problems. For example, your problems with playmates may have been settled by older people who stepped in to set things straight.

The more mature you become, the more problems you can handle on your own. But some problems may still be too serious or too complicated to solve by yourself. At times like these, it's smart to get help — from a parent, friend, teacher, counselor, social worker, doctor, or lawyer. You may need someone like this to solve a problem for you.

But be careful: If you ask for help because you're careless, lazy, or irresponsible, because you "don't feel like" dealing with your problem, or because you didn't plan ahead, you're being less than you could be. Also beware of asking for help too frequently, or the person you ask may eventually turn you down. Save your requests for times when you really need a hand.

ACTIVITY 32

Have you ever asked another person to fill in or "cover" for you?
YES ☐ NO ☐

If yes, what did you ask him or her to do?

_____

_____

_____

Why didn't you do it yourself?

_____

_____

_____

Did the person solve your problem? YES ☐ NO ☐

If yes, how?

_____

_____

Was this something you could have done yourself? YES ☐ NO ☐

Did you do anything to repay the person for helping you? YES ☐ NO ☐

If yes, what did you do?

_____

_____

_____

If no, why not?

_____

_____

_____

Are you in the habit of "rescuing" other people? YES ☐ NO ☐

If yes, why do you do it?

_____

_____

_____

If no, why not?

_____

_____

_____

_____

Something to think about

Some people continually let or even invite others to exploit *(take advantage of) them. Others learn to say "No." Where do* you *draw the line when someone keeps asking you for help and you can't or don't want to give it?*

ACTIVITY 33

PROBLEM-SOLVING STRATEGY 8: BRAINSTORMING

When you need to come up with a lot of ideas quickly, try brainstorming. The purpose of brainstorming is to generate as many ideas as you can, as fast as you can, without stopping to think about any of them. As long as you write your ideas down, you can sort them out later and decide which ones seem workable.

BRAINSTORMING TIPS:

• You can brainstorm alone with a pen and paper, or on a computer screen. Or you can brainstorm with other people — a friend, a group, a class at school, your family.

• Set a time limit — for example, five or ten minutes. Then write down *every* idea that comes to mind, no matter how crazy or impossible it seems. Stop when time is up.

• Sort the ideas, discarding the useless ones. Prioritize the rest in a list. Put the very best ideas at the top, and the weakest at the bottom.

On pages 97–99, you'll find three problems that need solutions. Brainstorm and prioritize ideas.

You can't find your term paper anywhere. You finished it last night, and now it's gone. It's due tomorrow.

BRAINSTORM what you can do.

1. _____

2. _____

3. _____

4. _____

5. _____

6. _____

7. _____

8. _____

9. _____

10. _____

Now PRIORITIZE the good ideas you came up with.

1. _____

2. _____

3. _____

4. _____

5. _____

ACTIVITY 33

You're at the store, about to buy a new pair of jeans. After waiting in line for half an hour, you realize that someone has picked your pocket and stolen your money.

BRAINSTORM what you can do.

1. _____
2. _____
3. _____
4. _____
5. _____
6. _____
7. _____
8. _____
9. _____
10. _____

Now PRIORITIZE the good ideas you came up with.

1. _____
2. _____
3. _____
4. _____
5. _____

You've heard a rumor that your girlfriend (or boyfriend) is interested in someone else. You check it out and learn that it's not just a rumor — it's a fact.

BRAINSTORM what you can do.

1. _____
2. _____
3. _____
4. _____
5. _____
6. _____
7. _____
8. _____
9. _____
10. _____

Now PRIORITIZE the good ideas you came up with.

1. _____
2. _____
3. _____
4. _____
5. _____

ACTIVITY 34

PROBLEM-SOLVING STRATEGY 9: TEAM UP

Term papers, tests, trouble at home — all these can be recurring stressors, disrupting your life again and again.

If this sounds familiar, maybe you need a partner. Learn how to find one by reading page 101. Then practice putting these ideas into action on pages 102 and 103.

Form an
A-Team

Find someone to *assist* you. Think of people whose *assets* (strengths) are the opposite of yours. For example:

• If you're weak in language but strong in science, find a study partner who's just the opposite.

• If you're good with people and not so good at coming up with ideas, find a partner who's just the opposite.

• If you're good at inventing, find a partner who's good at selling.

• If you take life too seriously, find a partner who looks at the funny side of things.

• If you're good at sports, find a partner who's good at music or art. (This doesn't mean that someone can't be good at sports *and* music or art.)

The point of forming an A-Team is to double your strengths and cancel out your weaknesses. You may even want to expand your twosome into a larger group.

Form an
S-Team

Pair up with someone who *shares* your problem. Then *support* each other. For example:

• If you're upset because your parents are divorcing, find a partner who has gone through (or is going through) the same experience.

• If you'd like to exercise more, but you never seem to get around to it, find a partner to exercise with you. That way you can encourage each other.

• If you have a habit you want to break, find a partner who wants to break the same habit.

• If you have work or studying to do or other responsibilities to fulfill, find a partner who has to do the same and work, study, or otherwise help each other.

The point of forming an S-Team is to develop a common bond — a source of strength in difficult or challenging times. Again, you may want to expand your twosome into a group of supportive friends.

ACTIVITY 34

**Form an
A-Team**

1. Describe a problem you could use some *assistance* with.

_____

_____

_____

2. Name one other person who could help you.

_____

3. Name any other people you could ask for help.

_____

_____

_____

_____

4. What will you contribute to the members of your A-Team?

_____

_____

_____

**Form an
S-Team**

1. Describe a problem you wish you could *share* with someone else.

_____

_____

_____

2. Name one other person who has the same problem.

_____

3. Name any other people you know about who have the same problem.

_____

_____

_____

_____

_____

4. How will you support the members of your S-Team?

_____

_____

_____

PROBLEM-SOLVING STRATEGY 10: LAUGHTER

Laughter is the best medicine.

Life poses many serious problems. But that doesn't mean you must take life seriously all the time. Learning to see the humorous side of life, and to laugh at yourself, may help you solve many of your problems.

Laughter, like exercise, produces the hormone endorphin in your body, which makes you feel good. Laughter often relieves distress in social situations and makes you more pleasant for others to be around. Laughter generates energy and stimulates creativity.

List five things that make you laugh.

_____

_____

_____

_____

_____

Describe a time when laughter helped you to relieve distress…

…in a social situation

_____

_____

…in a school or work setting

_____

_____

…in a family setting

_____

_____

…in another situation or setting

_____

_____

Something to think about

As you mature, laughter prevents hardening of the attitudes. It has also been said that he (or she) who laughs, lasts.

PROBLEM-SOLVING STRATEGY 11: USE CONSTRUCTIVE CRITICISM

If someone is causing a problem for you, it's usually best to talk directly to him or her about it. Often, people are reluctant to do this. They don't like to confront others because they're afraid this will create more problems. In fact, criticism can have positive results, as long as it's *constructive* and not *destructive*.

Constructive criticism "builds up"; destructive criticism "tears down." Constructive criticism leaves you feeling good about yourself and capable of making a positive change. Destructive criticism leaves you feeling so bad about yourself that even trying to change seems pointless.

Here's a step-by-step formula for giving someone constructive criticism, *in private*.

Step 1: Give the person two compliments. Be sincere and specific.

Step 2: Address the person using his or her name.

Step 3: In a pleasant tone of voice, and with a pleasant look on your face, state your criticism in one or two short, clear sentences.

Step 4: Tell the person what you would like him or her to do. Keep it simple. Set a time limit, if it's appropriate to do so.

Step 5: Offer your help, encouragement, and support.

Step 6: Thank the person for listening.

TIPS: Don't use this as an opportunity to drag up every gripe you've ever had about the person you're criticizing. Stay focused on *one* problem. And if the person wants your help, be sure to follow through within a time period you agree upon.

In real life, the other person will interrupt you, and this will become a dialogue. Listen and acknowledge the other person, but *stick to the formula.* Practice ahead of time so you can be sure to *stick to the formula no matter what the other person says.*

Page 108 gives an example of this strategy in action. Page 109 describes two problems. What could you say to offer constuctive criticism in each of these situations? Remember: Expect to be interrupted, but stick to the formula!

ACTIVITY 36

**CONSTRUCTIVE
CRITICISM
IN ACTION:
AN EXAMPLE**

You're annoyed because Terry, your sister (or brother), always takes long showers and never leaves any hot water for you. Here's how you handle the problem.

Step 1:

YOU: "I'm glad you're my sister (brother). I think it's great the way you let me borrow your new bike."

TERRY: "That's okay. It's no big deal. Just be sure to lock it up when you're done. And don't let any of your stupid friends ride it."

Steps 2 and 3:

YOU: "Terry, it really bothers me that you take so long in the shower in the morning. By the time I get to have my shower, there's no hot water left."

TERRY: "What do you mean? I just take an ordinary shower. It's not my fault that you get up later than I do. If you got up first instead of being so lazy all the time, you'd get the hot water."

Step 4:

YOU: "I'd appreciate it if you could keep your shower down to ten minutes from now on."

TERRY: "Give me a break! What am I, a human stopwatch?"

Step 5:

YOU: "I know it's hard to figure out how long you've been in the shower, so I've put the kitchen timer by the sink. You can set it for ten minutes when you get in. If you come out when the bell rings, there will be hot water for me, too."

TERRY: "Well, I guess I could try, if I remember. But you should get up earlier anyway. You're really lazy."

Step 6:

YOU: "Thanks a lot for helping me solve this problem. I really appreciate it."

1

Someone you know is always late.

Step 1: _____

_____

Steps 2 and 3: _____

_____

Step 4: _____

_____

Step 5: _____

_____

Step 6: _____

_____

2

Someone you know always interrupts you when you're talking.

Step 1: _____

_____

Steps 2 and 3: _____

_____

Step 4: _____

_____

Step 5: _____

_____

Step 6: _____

_____

*"If it's painful for you to criticize your friends,
you are safe in doing it.
If you take the slightest pleasure in it,
that's the time to hold your tongue."*
Alice D. Miller

ACTIVITY 37

PROBLEM-SOLVING STRATEGY 12: POSITIVE SELF-TALK

People are always talking to themselves. Most do their self-talking in the privacy of their own minds, or when they are alone.

Is your self-talk *positive* or *negative?* Does it boost or blast your self-esteem?

With practice, you can learn to use positive self-talk to comfort, motivate, or congratulate yourself. You can also use it to help you solve problems. You're more likely to make good decisions when you're feeling good about yourself and being encouraged.

With practice, you can learn to block out negative self-talk. You can choose not to listen, or to change negative statements into positive ones.

Read this list of self-talk statements. Which ones would make you feel better about yourself? Which ones would make you feel worse about yourself?

	Better	Worse
1. I can never win.	☐	☐
2. This time I'm going to do my best.	☐	☐
3. I didn't do it this time, but next time I will!	☐	☐
4. Nobody likes me.	☐	☐
5. A few people like me a lot.	☐	☐
6. At least one person really loves me.		
7. I can make friends, if I really try.	☐	☐
8. People like my sense of humor/good manners/ cute nose/_____.	☐	☐
9. I'm fat and ugly.	☐	☐
10. I'll look better when I lose some weight.	☐	☐
11. I'll take better care of myself starting today!	☐	☐
12. I can't do anything right. Nothing works for me.	☐	☐
13. I always do the best I can, even though my best isn't good enough.	☐	☐
14. I always do the best I can. Sometimes my best is good enough. I can do it!	☐	☐
15. Attitude, not aptitude, determines my altitude.	☐	☐
16. People say I have a nice _____.	☐	☐
17. If only I could _____.	☐	☐
18. I can _____.	☐	☐
19. I always do it this way!	☐	☐
20. Today I'll try something new.	☐	☐
21. I have to _____.	☐	☐
22. I want to _____.	☐	☐
23. If only _____.	☐	☐
24. I wish _____.	☐	☐
25. I did _____, but I'll never do it again.	☐	☐
26. I said _____, but I'll never say it again.	☐	☐
27. Although I did _____, I'll try to do _____ instead next time.	☐	☐

	Better	Worse
28. Although I said _____, I'll try to say _____ instead next time.	☐	☐
29. _____ isn't my fault. It's _____'s fault!	☐	☐
30. _____ isn't my fault, but I can help by _____.	☐	☐
31. Oh, no! I've done it again. I'm so stupid!	☐	☐
32. Everybody makes mistakes.	☐	☐
33. Why can't I be like _____, who never gets in trouble or makes mistakes?	☐	☐

What three *positive* statements work best for you?

1. _____

2. _____

3. _____

WATCH WHAT YOU SAY — YOU MAY BE LISTENING

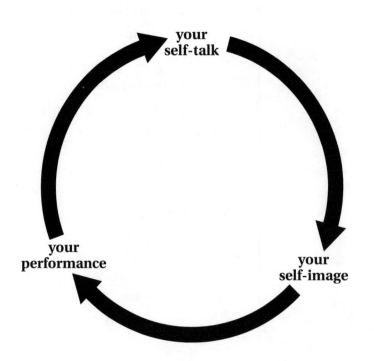

your self-talk

your self-image

your performance

PROBLEM-SOLVING STRATEGY 13: POSITIVE VISUALIZATION

Be the star of your own show!

Positive self-talk can help you overcome problems. So can positive visualization. Albert Einstein valued imagination more than knowledge when it came to unlocking the secrets of the universe.

Use your imagination as your "movie screen." Write the script and star in mini-films in which you…

a. act bravely

b. act cowardly

c. act lovingly

d. act selfishly

e. act wisely

f. act foolishly

g. act angrily

h. act to make peace

i. act in character

j. act out of character

ACTIVITY 38

Are there other feelings you'd like to act out? Script them here, then try them in your imagination.

_____

_____

_____

_____

_____

Think of a problem you'd like to solve. Write it as a film script and show it on your mental movie screen. Imagine four (or more) different endings. Then choose the one you like best, and rerun it to encourage yourself as you work toward that goal or solution in real life.

MY STORY

_____

_____

_____

_____

_____

_____

_____

_____

Ending One:

_____

_____

_____

_____

_____

Ending Two:

_____

_____

_____

_____

_____

Ending Three:

_____

_____

_____

_____

_____

Ending Four:

_____

_____

_____

_____

_____

Something to think about

Whether you think you can, or whether you think you can't — you're right!

YOUR NOTES AND THOUGHTS

ORDER FORM

QTY	TITLE	PRICE	TOTAL
	YOU AND STRESS	$8.95	
	YOU AND SCHOOL	$8.95	
	YOU AND YOUR FAMILY	$8.95	
	LEADER'S GUIDE	$6.95	
	MAKING THE MOST OF TODAY: Daily Readings for Young People on Self-Awareness, Creativity, and Self-Esteem	$8.95	
	PERFECTIONISM: What's Bad About Being Too Good?	$8.95	
	DIRECTORY OF AMERICAN YOUTH ORGANIZATIONS (1992–1993)	$18.95	
	GET OFF MY BRAIN: A Survival Guide For Lazy Students	$8.95	
	CAN YOU FIND IT? 25 Library Scavenger Hunts To Sharpen Your Research Skills	$12.95	
	Copies of the Free Spirit Catalog	FREE	FREE
(Minn. residents add 6.5% sales tax unless tax exempt)			
Shipping/handling ($3.00 for first book and $.50 for each additional book)			
TOTAL AMOUNT DUE			

To Order By Phone: 1(800)735-7323

Method of payment:

☐ Check enclosed ☐ P.O. Attached

☐ VISA ☐ MASTERCARD Good through _____

Card #: _____

Signature _____

Send to:

Name: _____

Address: _____

City/State/Zip _____

Daytime phone: (   ) _____

FREE SPIRIT PUBLISHING INC.
400 First Avenue North, Suite 616
Minneapolis, MN 55401